USS MINNEAPOLIS CA-36

WARSHIP PICTORIAL #2

CLASSIC WARSHIPS PUBLISHING

Editor - Steve Wiper
Layout - T.A.Flowers
Illustrations - T.A.Flowers

Look for these exciting subjects in future books from

CLASSIC WARSHIPS PUBLISHING

USS LOUISVILLE CA-28

Brooklyn Class Cruiser

Omaha Class Cruiser

Pensacola Class Cruiser

Atlanta Class Cruiser

Cleveland Class Cruiser

Copyright © 1997

**CLASSIC WARSHIPS
PUBLISHING**

P.O.Box 57591 • Tucson AZ 85732
ISBN # 0-9654829-1-X

Late 1934 - The heavy cruiser Minneapolis CA-36 berthed next to two of her sisters: the Astoria CA-34, center, and the New Orleans CA-32, right. A total of seven ships made up the New Orleans Class Heavy Cruisers, permitted by the Washington Treaty of 1922.

USS Minneapolis CA 36
New Orleans Class Cruiser

Operational history

1929

February 13 - "Cruiser Bill" became law, authorizing Portland, New Orleans and Brooklyn Class Cruisers.

1931

June 27 - Keel laid at Philadelphia Navy Yard.

1933

September 6 - Launched: christened by Miss Grace L. Newton.

1934

May 19 - Commissioned as CA-36 with Captain Gordon W. Haines as her first commanding officer.
July - Departed for European waters on her shakedown cruise.
September - Returns to Philadelphia Navy Yard for post shakedown yard service and alterations.

1935

April 4 - Sailed for the west coast via the Panama Canal.
April 18 - Arrived in San Diego, California to join Cruiser Division 6 as flagship.

1936

May - Collided with ore freighter SS Marore outside Panama Canal. Approximately 15 ft. of the bow was replaced. No serious injuries.

1937-39

Cruised the Pacific participating in various peacetime training exercises and Division maneuvers. Made single cruise to the Caribbean early in 1939.

1939

Transferred to Pearl Harbor, Hawaii, as flagship of 13 ship security patrol.

1940

April 4 - US Navy moved to Pearl Harbor, Hawaii, as a deterrent to further Japanese military expansion in the Far East.

1941

February 1 - US Fleet reformed into three fleets: Atlantic, Pacific and Asiatic.
December 7 - At sea for gunnery practice twenty miles off Pearl Harbor Hawaii. Also assisting in the filming of the motion picture "To the Shores of Tripoli." After report of the Japanese attack on Pearl Harbor, takes up patrol with the cruisers USS Detroit, St.Louis and Phoenix. This group is later joined by the carrier USS Enterprise but failed to make contact with the Japanese Strike Force.

1942

January - Joined carrier task force conducting raids on the Gilbert and Marshall Islands groups.
February 1 - While screening the carrier USS Lexington, assisted in the destruction of three enemy bombers.
February 20 - Screened fast carrier group conducting raids on Japanese shipping at Lae.
March 10 - Provided anti-aircraft cover for carrier group conducting raids on Japanese shipping at Salamaua.
May 4-8 - Again screened carriers USS Lexington and the USS Yorktown at the *Battle of Coral Sea.* Rescued survivors from Lexington when that ship was lost. Downed three more Japanese bombers.
June 3-6 - Once again provided air defense for carriers at the *Battle of Midway.* This major engagement was the war's turning point with the loss of four Japanese carriers and over 250 of her aircraft and crews.
August 31 - With the carriers at Guadalcanal to support the first Allied amphibious landings there. Towed the crippled carrier USS Saratoga from the battle area after that ship was hit by two torpedoes and could not launch or receive her aircraft.
September-October - Supported Allied landings west of Lunga Point and on Funafut.
November 30 - Sailed as flagship with four heavy cruisers and six destroyers of Task Force 67 off Guadalcanal. Engaged Japanese at the *Battle of Tassafaronga,* sinking enemy transport and helping to sink another. Took two torpedo hits from Japanese destroyers; one in #2 fireroom, the other destroyed the bow. 37 men killed. Limped to Tulagi at three knots.
December 5 - Endured nearly fatal secondary explosion while undergoing

repairs at Tulagi. Rigged with an emergency bow made of coconut tree logs, sailed for Esprito Santo.

1943

January - At Esprito Santo a temporary steel bow was fitted. Still very much a wounded ship, sailed alone for Pearl Harbor.

March 2 - Arrived at Pearl Harbor. Approximated 60ft. of new bow fitted. Left immediately for Mare Island, California, for further repairs.

April -Arrived at Mare Island to begin massive repair and refit which will take the better part of the next four months.

August - Returned to front line duty.

October 5 - Returned to active duty with the bombardment of Wake Island in support of Allied landings.

November 20-December 4 - Conducted island bombardment supporting assault on Makin Island in the Gilberts.

December - Screened fast carrier task force for the invasion of Kwajalein and Majuro.

1944

January-February - Supported landings throughout the Marshall Island group with shore bombardment and anti-aircraft cover.

March-April - Provided anti-aircraft fire for carriers in support of operations against Palau, Truk, Satawan and Ponape .

May - Resupplied at the recently captured island of Majuro.

June 14 - Shelled Saipan prior to landings of US Marines.

June19/20 - Called to join Task Force 58 to screen carriers in *Battle of Philippine Sea.* Incurred minor damage from a near miss of a Japanese bomb.

July 8/August 9 - Again called for bombardment duties prior to American invasion of Guam.

September 6-October 14 - Conducted shelling operations against Japanese defenders on Palau Island.

October 17 - Entered Leyte Gulf as part of large pre-invasion force. Confirmed five Japanese planes shot down.

October 24/25 - Was one of eight cruisers and six battleships which took part in the *Battle of Surigo Strait* off Leyte. The engagement nearly annihilated part of a giant 3-prong Japanese naval force sent to defend Leyte.

November-December - Returned to shore bombardment duties and group anti-aircraft defense covering the continued operations in the Philippines.

1945

January 4-18 - Supported Allied landings at Lingayen Gulf on Luzon.

February 13-18 - Supplied air cover and landing support for the invasion of the Bataan Peninsula and Corregidor Island.

March - Retired from front-line duty for resupply and preparation for the forthcoming assault on Okinawa.

March 25 - In support of a 10 battleship bombardment force, shelled Okinawa on a daily basis until the main Allied invasion on April 1.

April 12 - Helped to repel massive kamikaze attack aimed at Okinawa Invasion Fleet. Four suicide planes downed. Departed for the United States and much needed repairs later that night.

May - Arrived in Bremerton, Washington. During her refit at nearby Puget Sound, received new linings for the badly worn 8" gun barrels.

July - Returning to the pacific theater, the crew is entertained by movie actress Chili Williams during the stop in Pearl Harbor.

August - Anchored at Subic Bay, Philippines, when Japan surrendered on August 11.

September 9 - Flew the colors of Admiral Thomas Kincaid, who accepted the surrender of Japanese forces in Korea.

December - Transported US troops back to the United States.

1946

January 15 - Sailed for the East coast via the Panama Canal.

May 21 - Placed in reserve in the "Mothball Fleet" at the Philadelphia Navy Yard.

1947

February 10 - Officially decommissioned.

March 1 - Stricken from the US Navy roster.

1948-1958

In storage and virtually forgotten about.

1959

August 14 - Sold to the Union Metals and Alloys Corporation and sub-sequently scrapped.

Awarded a total of 17 Battle Stars

September 6, 1933: Philadelphia Navy Yard - A crowd gathers, including newsreel cameramen, as shipyard personnel prepare the Minneapolis for launching later the same day. The launching ceremonies will take place in the "bandstand" at the base of the bow which, if you look closely, has a slight bulb.

Early 1934: Philadelphia Navy Yard - The Cruiser Minneapolis nearing completion. Before she is commissioned, the range clock under the aft fire control position will be removed, to be replaced by a 12ft. rangefinder. A similar range clock forward will also be landed and its position used for observation.

April 4, 1935 - The Minneapolis sails from the Philadelphia Navy Yard bound for San Diego, California. Upon her arrival there on April 18 she became flagship of Cruiser Division 6. She wears a fresh coat of Navy Gray (a) and the crew has been mustered for the occasion.

USS Minneapolis in dry dock sometime in the mid 1930's, possibly after her European shakedown cruise(July, 1934). Scaffolding has been raised to give maintainence to the lower hull. Her two anchors lie at the bottom of the dry dock.

Circa 1935 - 5 in. 25 cal. dual purpose gun: secondary battery and anti-aircraft weapon found on most treaty heavy cruisers, older battleships and a few aircraft carriers. The piece in the photo is the #3 position on "Minnie's" starboard side, abreast the #1 funnel. The gun's maximum range was 14,500 yds at 45 degrees elevation and a maximum ceiling of 27,400 ft. at 85 degrees elevation. With a trained crew the 5 in. 25 cal. could fire 12-14 rounds a minute at a stationary target. Shell weight was about 54 lbs.

May, 1939 - This photo was taken from the aft fire control position, looking forward toward the #2 funnel. The two large pipes running up the back of the funnel vent auxiliary exhausts from the ship; the one on the right from the incinerator located at the base of the funnel. She is passing through the Panama Canal during Caribbean maneuvers.

The Minneapolis lies with other members of the Pacific Fleet probably at San Diego, California, in 1939. One of the captain's launches motors toward the camera after being lowered to the water by the starboard crane. The two huge cranes also handled the scouting float planes. Off her stern, an Omaha Class light cruiser.

September 15, 1941 - The Minneapolis strikes a beautiful pose just prior to the war. Her appearance is nearly the same as when she was built. The ship was painted in the pre-war Navy Gray (a) with metal decks in Dark Gray (c). The wood covering on the decks was of natural holley stoned teak. Blast bags on the 8in. guns and the funnel tops were black. The Mk.31 dual purpose directors have canvas over their open tops and are turned aft.

May 26, 1942: Pearl Harbor, Hawaii - The Minneapolis returns to port not long after her participation in the Battle of Coral Sea. She is painted Measure 11: overall Sea Blue with horizontal surfaces painted Deck Blue (20-B). The crew has not been mustered but everyone seems to be facing the camera.

August 31, 1942 - The Minneapolis prepares to take the aircraft carrier USS Saratoga in tow during the Battle of the Solomons. The "Sara" was hit by two Japanese torpedoes which rendered her unable to launch or receive aircraft. After being delivered to safety, the Saratoga was later able to launch the planes which sank the Japanese carrier Ryujo.

CVL RYUJO

December 1, 1942 - The Minneapolis sits in Ringbolt Harbor, Tulagi, after receiving two torpedo hits during the disastrous action at Tassafaronga the night before. One torpedo struck the port side at the #2 fireroom, the other nearly tore off the bow. The Cruiser Northampton and three destroyers were sunk and two other cruisers badly damaged.

The picture on page 19 shows her 5 days later after the damaged bow had been cut away back to the anchor chain pipes. A secondary gas explosion has caused further damage and she lost 7 feet of freeboard. Fortunately, there were no new casualties

December, 1942: Tulagi - The "Minnie" has undergone a major exercise in the art of camouflage. Crew members have covered the ship with camouflage netting and local vegetation to hide her from raiding Japanese aircraft. This is the aft part of the ship : the aircraft hanger to the right, the #3 turret hidden by palm fronds in the center and on the left, the barrels of one 40 mm mount on the stern pointing skyward.

December, 1942: Tulagi - In the process of repairs, the 36 in. searchlights have been removed as well as the shielding around most of the 5 in. guns. The crew of the Minneapolis, with the help of a US Seabee unit stationed on the island, will make all of the temporary repairs. She will leave for Esprito Santo with a bow made of logs from the native coconut trees.

March 3, 1943 - Minneapolis arrives at Pearl Harbor with the temporary steel bow which had been fitted at Esprito Santo. The unusual parallel shapes on the bridge wings are wind deflectors. Notice the painted camouflage on the yard crane.

March 9, 1943: Pearl Harbor - Finally into dry dock and awaiting a new bow. The temporary bow has been removed except for a few twisted plates at the bottom. Shipyard personnel suspended by scaffolding repair the outer hull where the second torpedo struck, killing everyone except one man, in the first three firerooms.

April 11, 1943: Pearl Harbor, Hawaii - USS Minneapolis leaving port after repair of major damage. The facilities at Mare Island are needed to finish repairs and give her a complete overhaul. She is apparently capable of only partial power as the #1 funnel is capped off with canvas. The stern 40mm mounts which were removed during repairs were not returned. Notice lack of anchor on the new bow.

May 1, 1943: Mare Island, California - The Minneapolis lies dockside awaiting her turn for repairs. This photograph and the one on page 26 are enlargements of the backgrounds of two photographs of the USS Indianapolis CA 35. (See Warship Pictorial #1, p. 25)

May 1, 1943: Mare Island - A very sick Minneapolis. The Japanese 24 in. (Long Lance) torpedo was a powerful weapon. The two hits that the Minneapolis took could have sunk her (like the Northampton) but even so, the damage was extensive. At this stage of repairs, the ship has been stripped. Missing are the #1 funnel, the starboard catapult, the bridge 1.1 in. anti-aircraft guns, the searchlights and part of the tower, the 12 ft. range finder and the wings from the two upper bridge levels.

September 4, 1943: Mare Island, California - The Minneapolis shortly after her extensive rebuilding. Immediately noticeable is the reduction in the width of the bridge, done to reduce top weight, lower the center of gravity and increase the arc of fire for her anti-aircraft guns. The two 26ft. motor whale boats tied to the boom are the only small boats she now carries.

September 4, 1943 - The Minneapolis looks quite a bit different than when she entered Mare Island four months prior. Along with major damage repair, the Minneapolis received a complete refit and a strange new paint scheme.

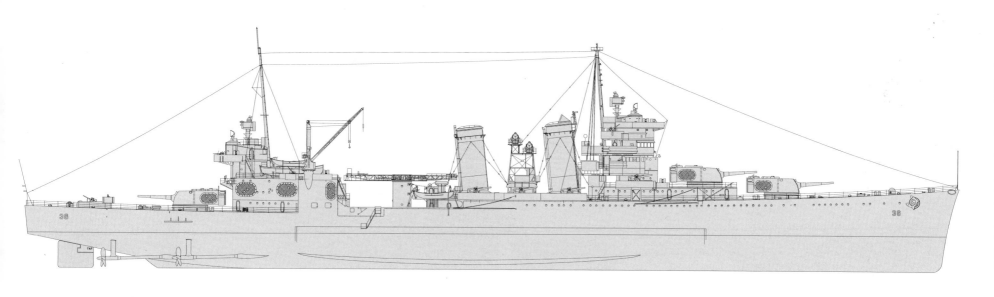

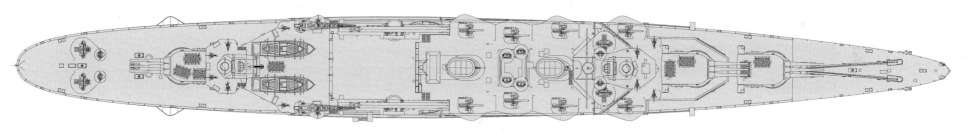

Minneapolis at the *Battle of the Solomons*
August, 1942

scale 1/700

27

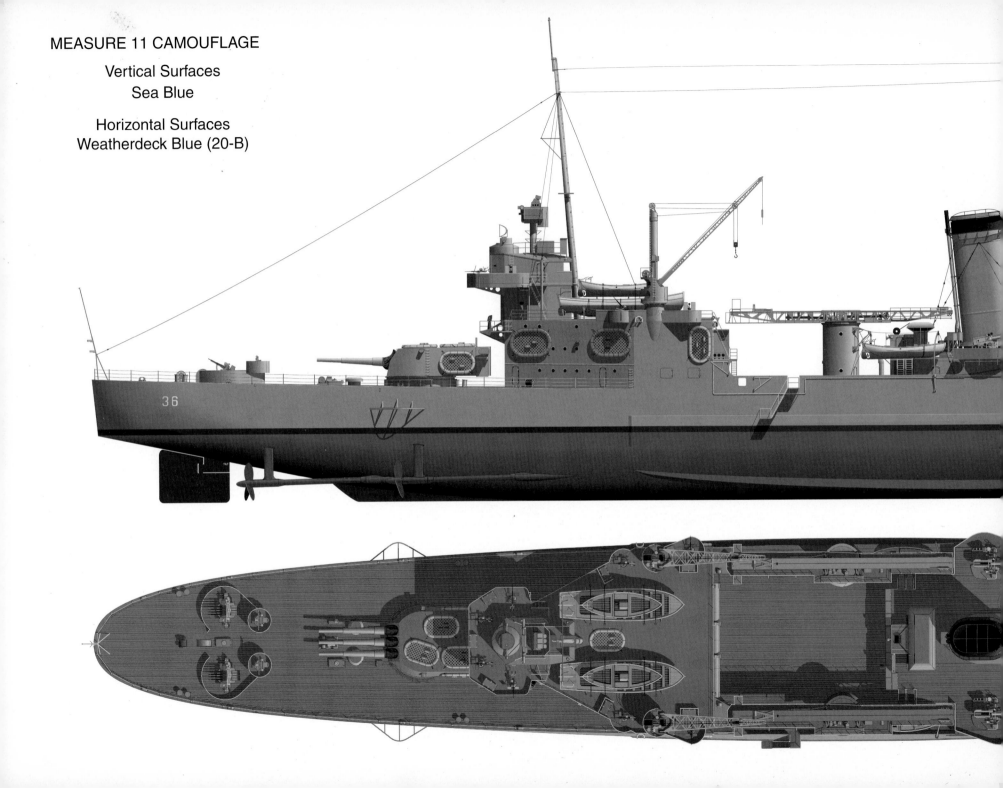

MEASURE 11 CAMOUFLAGE

Vertical Surfaces
Sea Blue

Horizontal Surfaces
Weatherdeck Blue (20-B)

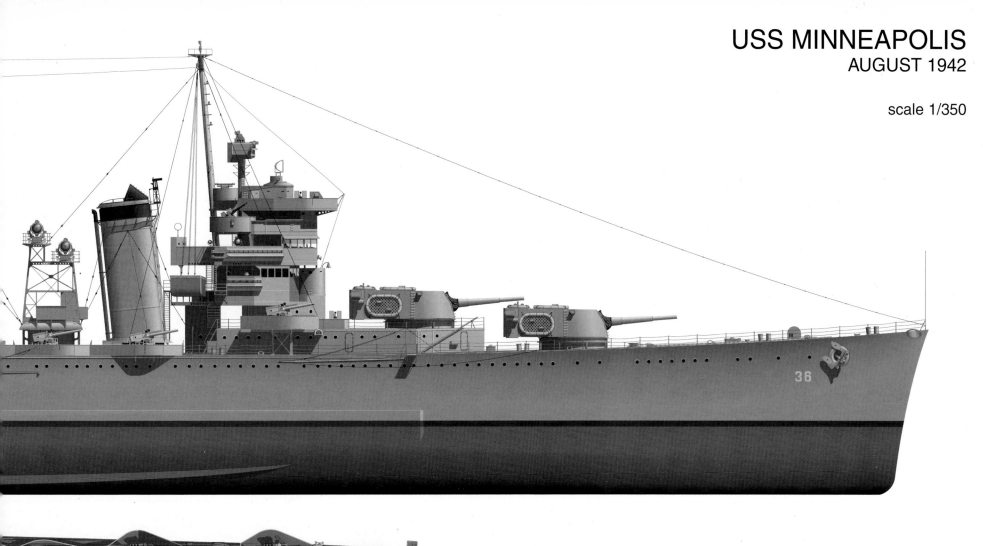

USS MINNEAPOLIS
AUGUST 1942

scale 1/350

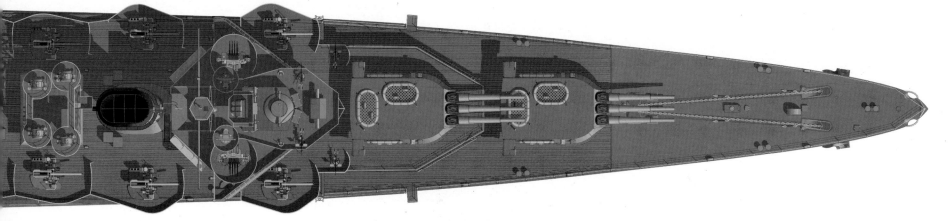

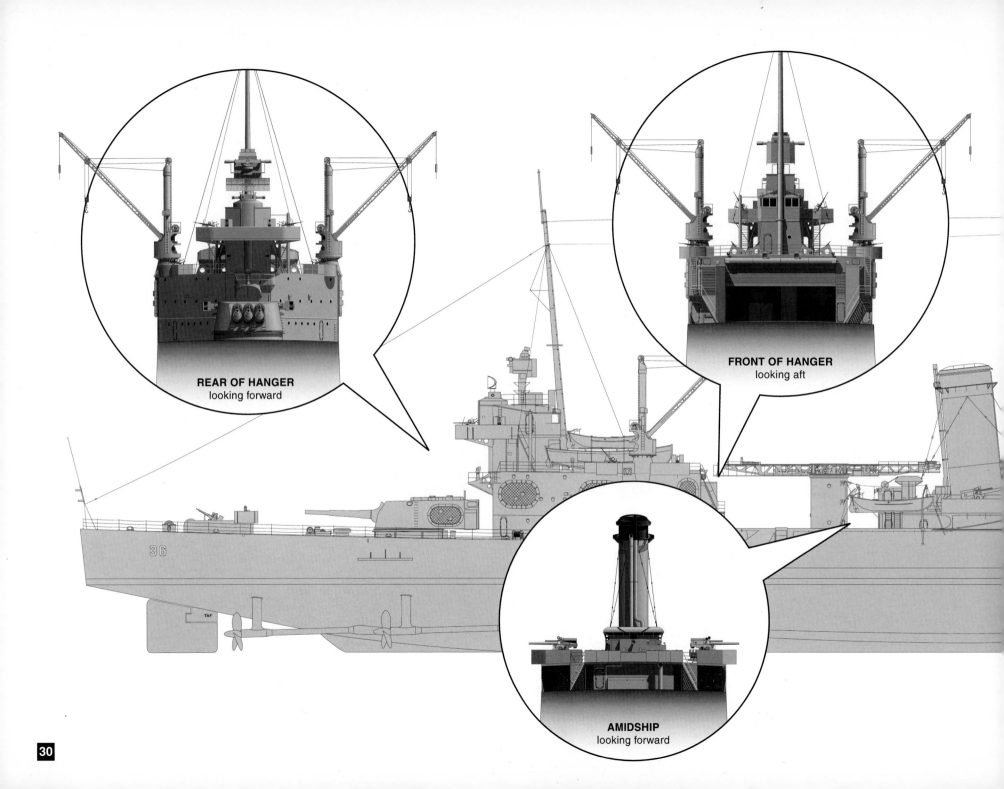

REAR OF HANGER
looking forward

FRONT OF HANGER
looking aft

AMIDSHIP
looking forward

36

USS MINNEAPOLIS

OCTOBER, 1942

SCALE 1/350

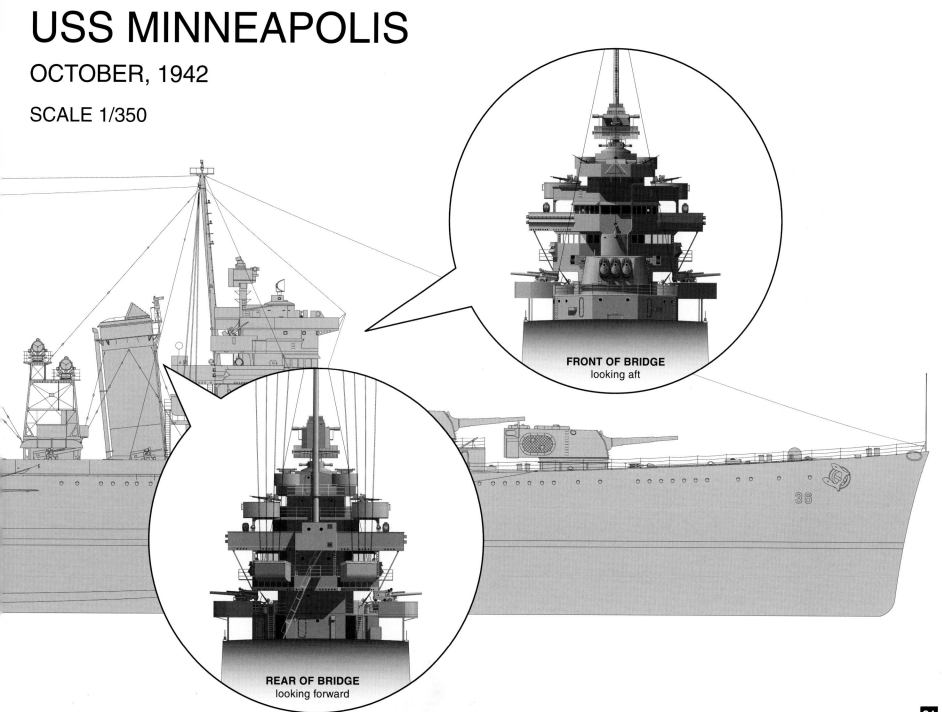

FRONT OF BRIDGE
looking aft

REAR OF BRIDGE
looking forward

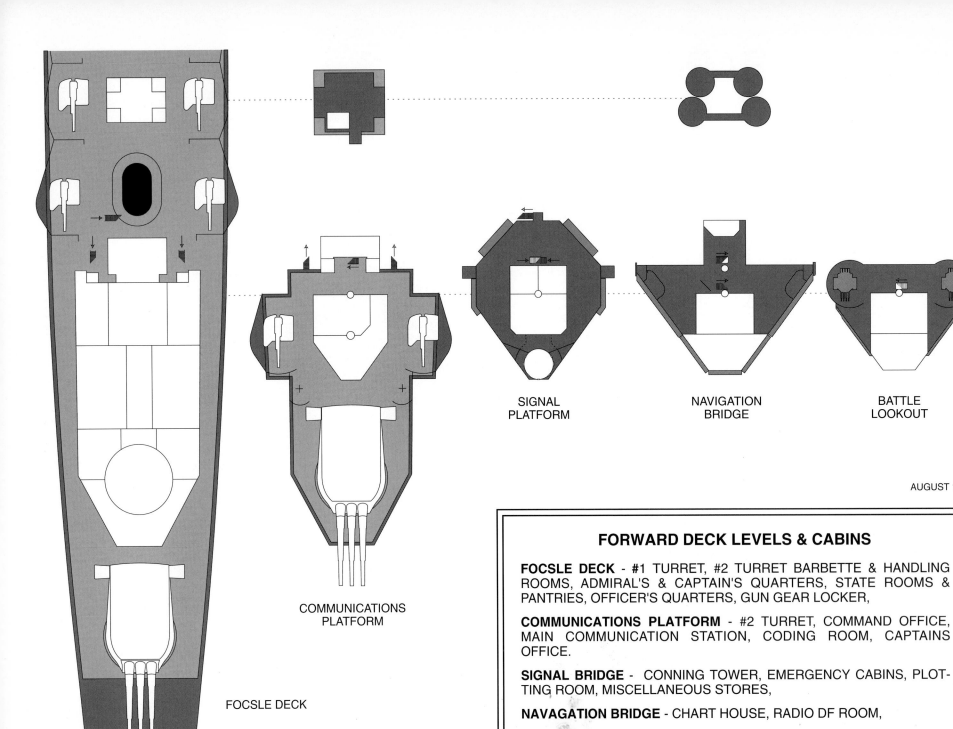

SIGNAL
PLATFORM

NAVIGATION
BRIDGE

BATTLE
LOOKOUT

AUGUST 1942

COMMUNICATIONS
PLATFORM

FOCSLE DECK

FORWARD DECK LEVELS & CABINS

FOCSLE DECK - #1 TURRET, #2 TURRET BARBETTE & HANDLING ROOMS, ADMIRAL'S & CAPTAIN'S QUARTERS, STATE ROOMS & PANTRIES, OFFICER'S QUARTERS, GUN GEAR LOCKER,

COMMUNICATIONS PLATFORM - #2 TURRET, COMMAND OFFICE, MAIN COMMUNICATION STATION, CODING ROOM, CAPTAINS OFFICE.

SIGNAL BRIDGE - CONNING TOWER, EMERGENCY CABINS, PLOTTING ROOM, MISCELLANEOUS STORES,

NAVAGATION BRIDGE - CHART HOUSE, RADIO DF ROOM,

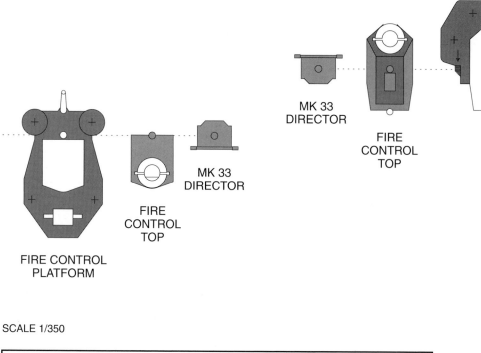

FIRE
CONTROL
PLATFORM

MK 33
DIRECTOR

FIRE
CONTROL
TOP

MK 33
DIRECTOR

FIRE
CONTROL
TOP

FIRE
CONTROL
PLATFORM

FIRE CONTROL
PLATFORM

SCALE 1/350

HANDGER
DECK

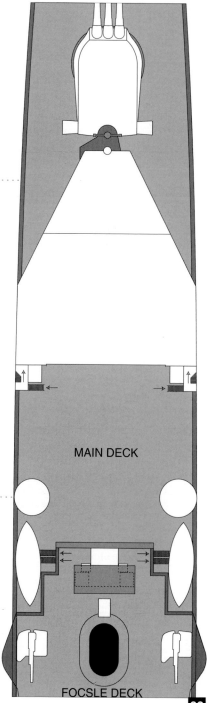

MAIN DECK

FOCSLE DECK

MIDSHIP & AFT DECK LEVELS & CABINS

MAIN DECK - #3 TURRET, AIRCRAFT HANGER SPACES, CATAPULT TOWERS, SMALL BOAT STORAGE, AVIATION WORKSHOP & STOREROOM, CREW'S WASHROOMS & W.C.

HANGER DECK - AIRCRAFT CATAPULTS, MOTOR LAUNCH STORAGE, HANDLING CRANES, 20mm AIRCRAFT DEFENCE,

FIRE CONTROL PLATFORM - AFT FIRE CONTROL STATION, RADAR ROOM, SECONDARY STEERING, 20mm AIRCRAFT DEFENCE,

September 4, 1943 - *The new camouflage pattern is a variation of Measure 8, intended to make the profile appear more like a (Benson Class) destroyer. Notice the false sheer line and the two huge "life rafts". The funnels were made to appear smaller by painting the back sides darker. Various deck fittings and structures were dappled and feathered to break up their lines. The starboard crane has been landed and one of the new quad 40mm guns replaces it.*

September, 1943 - Circled forward are two new 20mm guns. On turrets #1 & #2 floater nets replace life rafts. Around the bridge base are more 20mm singles and on the signal platform, new quad 40mm guns. Atop the fire control station sits the Mk31 main gun director with a Mk3 radar screen. Situated on it's own pedestal behind, sits the dual purpose director, Mk33. The huge windows around the navigation bridge are simply painted rectangles, part of the camouflage scheme.

USS MINNEAPOLIS
OCTOBER 1943

scale 1/350

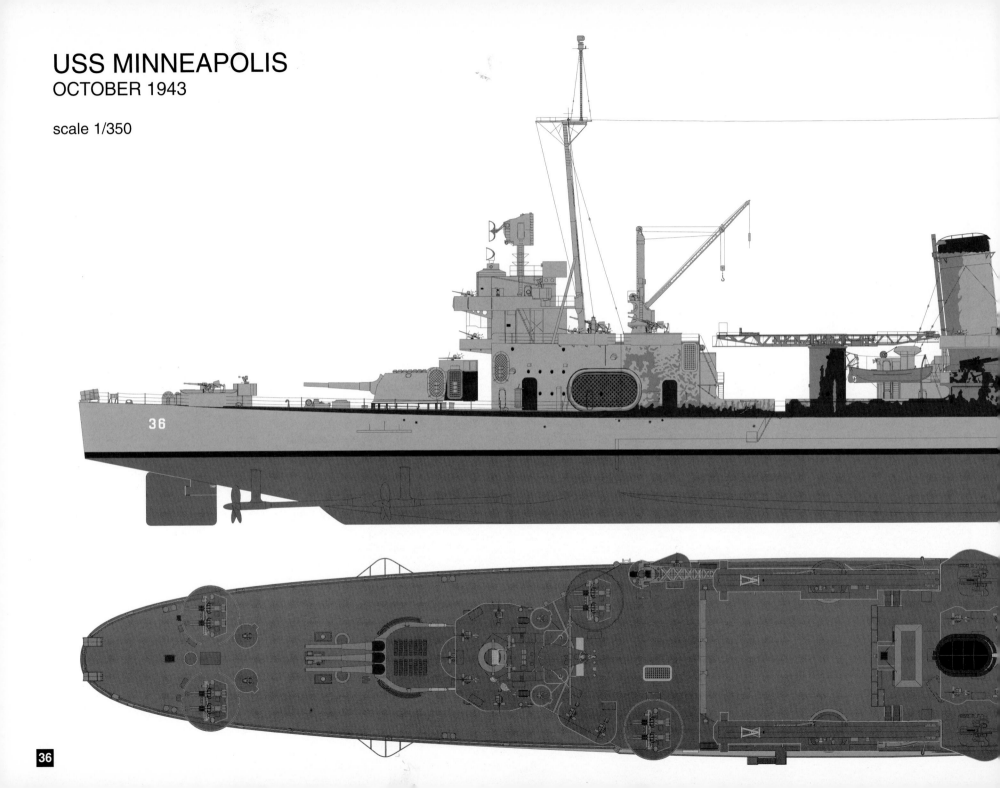

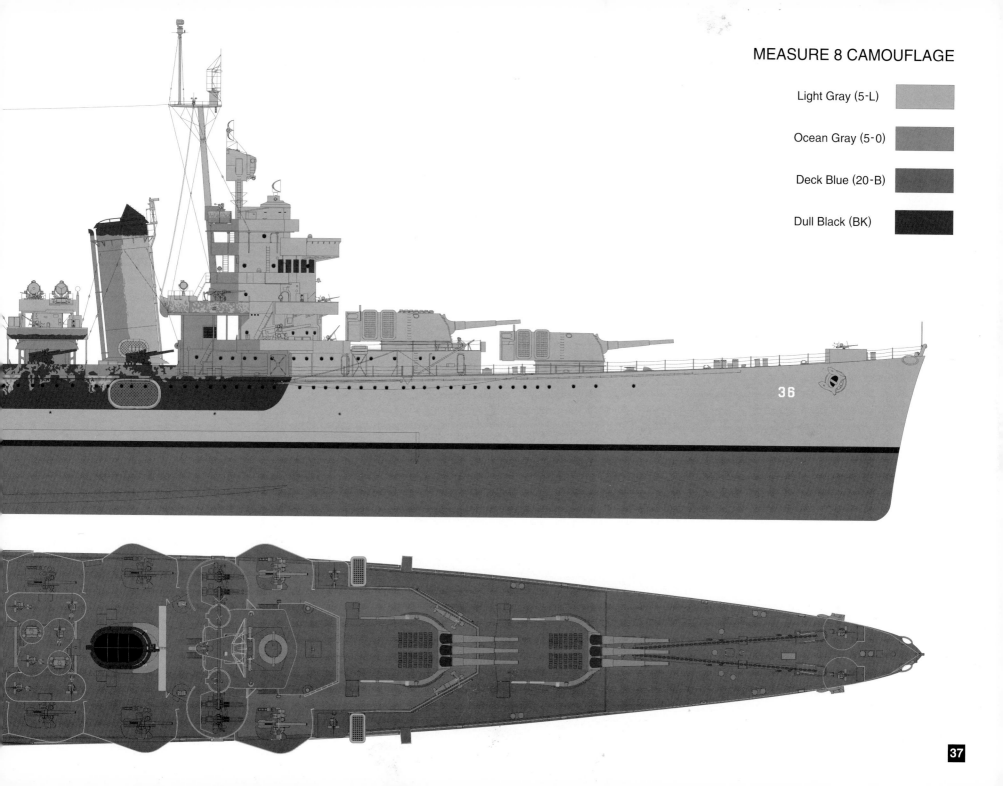

MEASURE 8 CAMOUFLAGE

Light Gray (5-L)

Ocean Gray (5-0)

Deck Blue (20-B)

Dull Black (BK)

36

September, 1943 - Looking aft between the funnels, the original searchlight platform has been shortened and two 36 in. searchlights have been replaced by two 20mm singles. Lower down, room has been made to accommodate four more 20mm mounts. A new platform around #2 funnel holds four more new 20mm mounts. Over the aircraft hanger, new 40mm and additional 20mm guns. The aft fire control platform has been enlarged and the main mast shortened.

September 1943 - Looking forward from the catapults is another view of the new construction between the funnels. The narrowed bridge has helped to reduce top weight and lower the center of gravity. Atop the foremast is a new SK radar "mattress" and above it, the small SG radar unit.

September 1943 - Two quad 40mm mounts have been returned to their former position on the stern. A new 20mm mount sits in its tub on #3 turret and two more on the small platform just above. The new positions on the aft fire control platform contain the Mk51 directors for the new quad 40mm guns on the hanger.

September, 1943 - The starboard crane has been removed mainly to reduce topside weight. Besides some shore bombardment, her duties now largely consisted of screening aircraft carriers and her anti-aircraft compliment rose accordingly. She now sported 24 40mm guns and 28 20mm guns. Like the arrangement on the forward superstructure, she carries a Mk 31 main battery director with Mk 3 radar. Above that, partially covered with canvas, the Mk 33 DP director and Mk 4 radar.

October 5, 1943: Off Wake Island - These two photos were taken the day of the assault to capture Wake Island. At left, a Curtiss SOC is being lowered onto the port catapult. It will be launched to provide spotting for the Minneapolis' 8in. and 5in. bombardment, prior to Allied invasion. Below, an SOC has just been launched from the port catapult on a similar mission, this "Seagull" however carries two 100lb. bombs.

October 5, 1943 - The crew cleans the 8in. barrels after the day's shelling of Wake Island. The large blast bags, usually a dull black color, have faded noticeably from the salt air and intense sun.

October 10, 1943 - This overhead view taken from a flight of SBD's, shows a sleek and powerful warship. In the course of the next 22 months, the Minneapolis will participate in many of the major naval engagement while on her way to earning 17 Battle Stars.

USS MINNEAPOLIS

JUNE 1945

scale 1/350

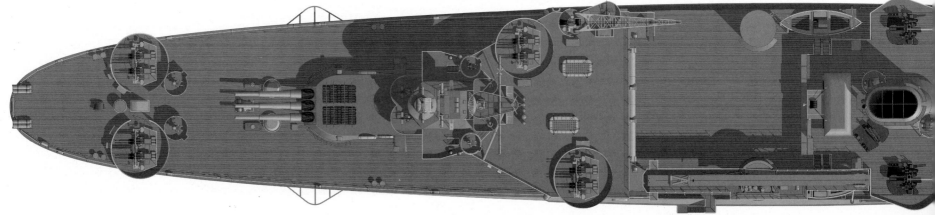

MEASURE 22 CAMOUFLAGE

Vertical Serfaces
Haze Gray (5-H)
Navy Blue (5-N)
Horizontal Surfaces
Weatherdeck Blue (20-B)

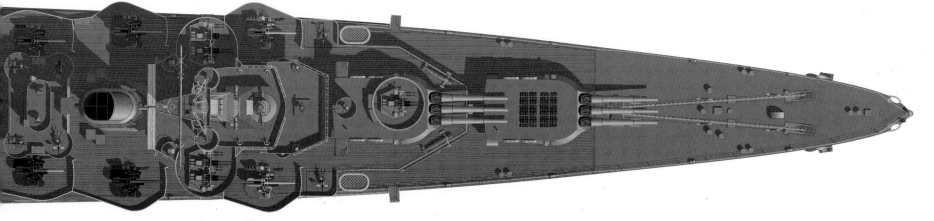

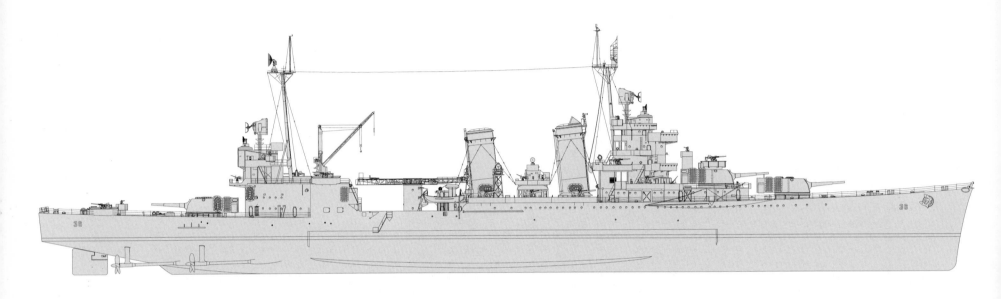

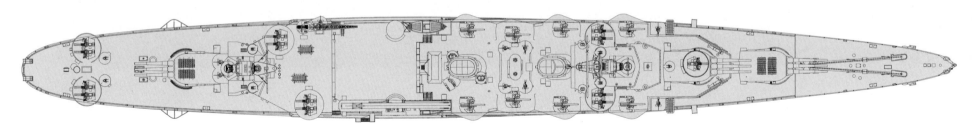

Minneapolis in final configuration
June 1945

scale 1/700

June 27, 1945: Puget Sound, Washington. The USS Minneapolis after her final refit. New is the 40mm twin on the #2 turret and the Mk. 51 director on a tall pedestal behind. Gone are the 20mm guns on the bow and the signal bridge. Her camouflage is now the "false horizon", Measure 22.

June 27, 1945: Puget Sound, Washington - To remove excessive weight, the port cata-pult has been removed, but the tower remains. The four SOC's she previously carried have been replaced by two of the newer SC-1 Seahawks. The Minneapolis soon departs for Pearl Harbor on her way back to the Pacific Theater.

June 27, 1945 - Part of the aft fire control platform has been removed as well as the 20mm position on #3 turret. By this time, the only remaining Japanese air threat was the the suicide "kamakaze" plane for which the 20mm gun was practically worthless. All but eight of her 28 20mm guns have been removed. A new SP fighter control radar screen sits atop the mainmast just above the American flag. The stern SC radar unit has been removed.

52

1945 - A photograph taken from the Mk.33 main gun director looking forward. Members of the crew take advantage of good weather to air out bedding. The circular screen at the bottom of the picture is the newly installed Mk.18 radar upgrade. Notice the 40mm mount is off–set, left of center on #2 turret and the absence of rangefinder arms on #1 turret.

53

Summer, 1945: The horrors of World War Two will soon be over as well as the career of the USS Minneapolis. She and her crews served their country proud. She will briefly ferry American personnel back to the United States and then be decommissioned shortly afterwards. She will end her days at the hands of the steel scrappers leaving very little to show for her gallant effort.

Authorized
February 13, 1929

Builder
Philadelphia Naval Shipyard
Philadelphia, Pennsylvania

Keel Laid
June 27, 1931

Launched
September 6, 1933

Commissioned
May 19, 1934

Dimensions
length overall ....588.25 ft.
length waterline ....578 ft.
beam ....61.75 ft.
draught (min.)............21.75 ft.
            (max.).............24.5 ft.

Displacement
standard.................10,315 tons
normal ....11,585 tons
full load - 1932........12,411 tons
            1944........13,719 tons

Armor
main belt ....3 to 5 in.
decks ....2.25 in.
turrets..................1.5 to 8 in.
magazines ....5 in.
conning tower...............5 in.

Aircraft
1934 - 1936..........Vought O3U Corsair (4)
1936 - 1945 ....Curtiss SOC Seagull (4)
1945.................Curtiss SC-1 Seahawk (2)

Compliment
1932 ....51 officers 700 enlisted men
1945 ....77 officers 965 enlisted men

Propulsion
Boilers ....White-Forster water tube type
Engines ....4 Parsons geared turbines
Speed ....32.75 kts. at 107,000 shp.

Fuel
standard.................1267 tons
full load - 1934 ....1900 tons
                1945 ....2240 tons

Endurance
1934 ......9,000 nm. at 15 kts.
1945 ......7,775 nm. at 15 kts.
            5,725 nm. at 20 kts.

Decommissioned
February 10, 1947

Cost to build
$11.25 million (1932)

ARMAMENT SUMMARY		1934	1942	1943	1944	1945
main battery	8 in./55 cal.	9	9	9	9	9
heavy anti-aircraft	5 in./25 cal.	8	8	8	8	8
light anti-aircraft	40 mm.	–	0 to 8	8 to 24	24	24 to 26
	20 mm.	–	6 to 12	12 to 28	28	8
	1.1 in.	–	16 to 8	8 to 0	–	–
	.50 cal.	8	8 to 0	–	–	–

REFERENCES

American Cruisers of WWII: S. Ewing
Cruisers of WWII: M.J. Whitley
Faces and Phases of the USS Minneapolis:
G.A. Stephens
Fighting Ships: Maclean & Poole
U.S.Cruisers: N. Friedman
U.S. Naval Weapons: N. Friedman

RESOURCES

United States Navy
U.S. Naval Historical Center
Tom Walkowiak's Floating Drydock
Real War Photos

CLASSIC WARSHIPS PUBLISHING

extends a very special thanks to

G.A.Stevens & The USS Minneapolis
Survivors Association
and
A.D.Baker III

Listed below are some of our favorite sources for reference books, photographs, plans and models

REAL WAR PHOTOS
P.O.Box 728
Hammond, Indiana 46325
catalog $3

PACIFIC FRONT HOBBIES
11804 NE 138th Street
Kirkland, Washington 98034
Ph. 206-821-2564

THE FLOATING DRYDOCK
c. o. general delivery
Kresgeville, Pennsylvania 18333
catalog $10

U. S. NAVAL INSTITUTE
2062 Generals Hwy.
Annapolis, Maryland 21401
Ph. 800-233-8764

TAUBMAN PLANS SERVICE
11 College Drive #4
Jersey City, New Jersey 07305
catalog $10

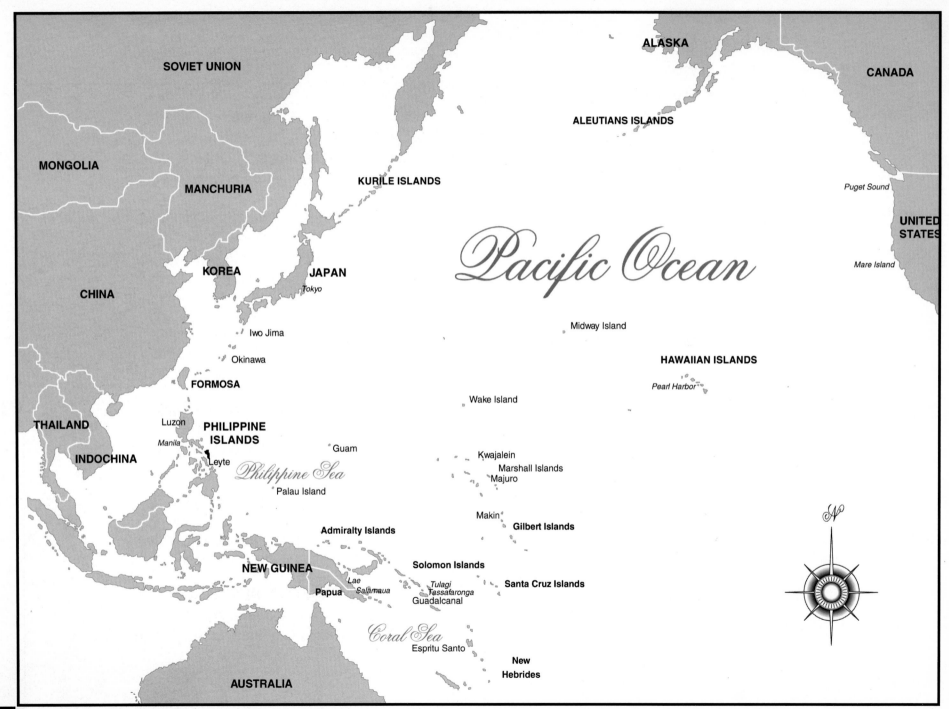